AUSTRALIA'S
Flowers and Trees

AUSTRALIA'S
Flowers and Trees

Text by Neil Hermes

AUSTRALIAN
PICTURE LIBRARY

C&A CHILD &
ASSOCIATES
AN ALL-AUSTRALIAN PUBLISHER

Front cover: The Cazneaux tree. (See page 25.)
Front cover, inset top: Boxleaf wattle. (See page 18.)
Front cover, inset bottom: Cooktown orchid.
          (See page 13.)
Back cover: The Gippsland waratah. (See page 10.)

Published by
Child & Associates Publishing Pty Ltd
5 Skyline Place, Frenchs Forest, NSW, Australia 2086
A wholly owned Australian publishing company
This book has been edited, designed
and typeset in Australia by the Publisher
Distributed by Gordon & Gotch Limited, Sydney

First edition 1988
Text by Neil Hermes
Captions by Dalys Newman
Photographs from the Australian Picture Library
© Australian Picture Library 1988
Printed in Hong Kong by South Sea International
Typesetting processed by Deblaere Typesetting Pty Ltd
Also published as part of *Australia: Land of Colour*

**National Library of Australia
Cataloguing-in-Publication**

Hermes, Neil.
    Australia's flowers & tress.

    ISBN 0 86777 196 8.

    1. Flowers – Australia. 2. Flowers – Australia
    – Pictorial works. 3. Trees – Australia. 4.
    Trees – Australia – Pictorial works. I. Newman,
    Dalys. II. Australian Picture Library. III. Title.

581.994

Australia's Flowers and Trees

Most of Australia's flowering trees are evergreen, which immediately separates them from the deciduous flowering trees of the Northern Hemisphere. In fact, Australia's forests and bushlands are dominated by members of two evergreen groups: the acacias and the eucalypts. Australia's plants have a strong similarity to the species dominant in South Africa and South America. For example, the southern continents are the centre of distribution for the proteas which include the Australian grevilleas, waratahs and banksias.

The deserts of Australia are the most diverse arid lands in the Southern Hemisphere. The plants found here contain a blend of ancient Australian stock combined with recent, geologically speaking, cosmopolitan species. There are few succulent species like cactus and most Australian arid plants have a range of techniques to withstand severe dehydration. Many desert species survive arid times as seed and only grow and flower following rain.

Australia's alpine flora, despite being restricted in area, carry a rare combination of ancient Southern Hemisphere plants and adapted modern ones.

Otherwise, the antipodean flora are dominated by the hard-leaved shrubs and trees typical of the poor soils of the south-east and south-west. The seasonal flowering of these highly diverse plant communities appealed to the first botanists as it does to thousands of tourists today.

The strange 'bush', as Australian forests are known, of the new continent was, to most of the first settlers, a major obstacle to be cleared away to make way for food-producing crops. Most of the first clearings around Sydney, however, produced very little food and became ugly 'bad lands'. Fortunately for the hungry colony fertile land was soon discovered at Parramatta and good crops were able to grow. However, the perception of the bush being a worthless obstacle has unfortunately become embedded in the national psyche. Many Australians still look to European or tropical landscapes to find beauty in plants. It is encouraging that at least one First Fleeter perceived the natural beauty of the flora of his new home. Captain Tench observed that

a variety of flowering shrubs abound, most of them entirely new to a European, and surpassing in beauty, fragrance and number, all I ever saw in an uncultivated state...[these] deserve the highest admiration and panegyric.

Gondwanaland

To understand the reasons for the appearance of the plant life of Australia it is useful to look back to the world as it was 200 million years ago. Then, South America, Africa, India, Antarctica and Australia were one vast continent. This continent of Gondwanaland began to break up around 110 million years ago by a process known as continental drift. As Australia moved slowly northward and the continent became more arid many of the original plants adapted to the new conditions. But many plants whose origins were in the cool, wet landmass of Gondwanaland continue to survive only in the moist areas of south-eastern Australia and Tasmania. Related plants can still be found in modern South America, South Africa and New Zealand. Their fossils are now found beneath the Antarctic ice.

The famous biologist Charles Darwin remarked in 1859 on the similarity between the flora of the south-western corner of Australia and the Cape of Good Hope...this will, no doubt, some day be explained.

It took over a century for the theory of continental drift to be proposed and supported before Darwin's explanation was found.

Typical of the ancient Gondwanaland plants is the magnificent huon pine which grows in the cold and wet river basins of western Tasmania. The huon pine has long been a highly sought-after timber tree and has been used for boat building and other specialist joinery purposes.

Huon pines can grow to 35 metres in height and a metre in diameter. Unfortunately huon pines are now very scarce both from previous logging and from the flooding of some rivers in dam construction.

What happened to Australia's plant life as the continent began moving towards the Equator about 110 million years ago?

At first, vast rainforests continued to cover the continent. Huon pines have been recorded in fossil deposits throughout Australia's current deserts. Slowly, as the rainfall became more erratic, new drier vegetation types increased in number. These were the eucalypts, wattles, casuarinas and callitris pines. Fire became an important factor in the spread of plant species and the incidence of fire increased with the arrival of Aborigines up to 100 000 years ago. The fire-sensitive species such as casuarinas and callitris pines were confined, and the fire-tolerant species like eucalypts and wattles spread more rapidly. Fire also continued to limit the spread of rainforest species in all parts of the country.

Plants species do not occur at random. Plants are usually found growing together in communities. These are given names such as rainforest, open forest, woodland and heath.

In Australia, rainforests occur in high-rainfall coastal parts of Queensland, New South Wales and western Tasmania. Rainforests are places of extraordinary plant richness. In the rainforest of the Atherton Tableland in northern Queensland, 164 different tree species were recorded in a plot 30 metres square. The northern rainforests are also rich in vines and large buttressed trees. About 75 per cent of all Australia's rainforests have been cleared. Animal production, sugarcane, bananas and potatoes are the main crops. One large area of rainforest around Lismore in New South Wales was known to the first settlers as the 'Big Scrub'. Less than half a per cent of the 750 square kilometres of that forest remains today.

The most common Australian forest types are the open forests so typical of much of the eastern coast from Cape York to Melbourne. Tall eucalypts dominate. These forests are subject to frequent summer fires. It was one of these coastal eucalypt forests that the early Polish botanist John Lhotsky said was of 'mind blunting monotony'. Even the great and perceptive biologist Charles Darwin said that the long strands of eucalypt bark gave the woods 'a desolate and untidy appearance'.

Darwin had been away from his native English home for four years and could perhaps have been forgiven his homesickness. These forests contain some of this country's most beautiful and most valuable trees such as the mountain ash of Victoria and the jarrah in Western Australia.

Other major vegetation communities include the woodlands, which have been largely taken over by sheep and wheat farms. These are areas of greatest eucalypt variety and where many native tussock grasses are to be found. The low bush country of much of Australia's inland is diverse in its plant life despite its apparent sameness.

Of surprise to many people is that much of the inland is in fact well covered in plants including extensive woodlands and shrublands. The species found in these areas include a variety of eucalypts, native pines and mulga. Some of the shrublands are of great importance for pastoral activities. About 6 per cent of the continent is bluebush and saltbush shrubland and this supports more than 2.5 million sheep.

Two of the major threats to the continued survival of many of these distinctive Australian arid land communities are the depredations of the introduced rabbit and agricultural mismanagement.

The impression many people have of inland Australia is a vast open country covered in grasses and herbs. This is usually the exception, although areas of grasslands do occur in the north, from the Kimberleys to the Barkly Tableland. These plains are covered in Mitchell grass which forms the basis of the northern pastoral industries.

Eucalypts, or gum trees as they are usually known, are some of the most visible of Australia's plants. The eucalypts form the dominant forest tree in about a third of the country. They are a uniquely Australasian plant. Six hundred different species are known and they grow naturally only in Australia and New Guinea and some nearby islands. Curiously, no eucalypts are known in New Zealand or the islands of the south-west Pacific.

The word eucalypt comes from the Greek words for 'well covered' and refers to the little lids that cover the emerging flowers. If it wasn't for these lids the famous May Gibbs storybook characters, Snugglepot and Cuddlepie, wouldn't have hats to wear!

Eucalypts are evergreen plants which are usually trees and many are quite large. The tallest is the mountain ash of Victoria and Tasmania. Trees of 100 metres in height are known. The mountain ash is exceeded in height only by the redwoods of California, which are the tallest trees in the world. Other massive trees include the Western Australian karri and the flooded gum of New South Wales, which both reach about 70 metres in height. Some species such as the narrow-leafed Sally, found in the Blue Mountains are hardly more than shrubs.

About forty species of eucalypts have an unusual and highly distinctive growth form. These are the mallees. They do not have a single trunk but many trunks emerging from the ground. Some eucalypts grow only in the mallee shape; some species which are usually well-formed trees will grow in the mallee shape on infertile sites. Several inland eucalypts which grow in the mallee shape are so widespread that the name mallee now also refers to this type of low inland forest.

One of the remarkable features of the eucalypts is the amazing sameness of the adult leaves of the hundreds of species. They generally have even-coloured, long and downward-hanging leaves. Many species have contrasting juvenile leaves that have features which are useful to the botanist in classifying the various types.

Not all of the eucalypt's leaf buds are used as the tree grows. Some remain concealed in the branches and trunk. When the tree is under stress, such as in drought, after fire, during insect attack or after pruning, the tree is then able to send out new shoots from the trunk and branches.

Eucalypts have developed strategies to withstand droughts which are unlike the methods used by dry-country plants in other continents such as the cactuses. Eucalypts have wide-ranging roots which are highly efficient at finding water. They have hard tissues in the stems and leaves which stop wilting. In the tropics some eucalypts even lose their leaves as the Dry Season progresses.

The eucalypts are also well adapted to survive the inevitable fires of the Australian bush. The bark on most eucalypts is very thick and provides good insulation for the deeper living tissues. Most large trees are not killed in a fire even when all the leaves and smaller branches are removed and the bark is totally blackened. The new leaf buds will soon emerge from the bark and branches. In a less severe fire the leaves may be merely replaced. In a still less severe fire adult trees may survive totally unscathed and only the young seedlings will be killed.

Some trees have adapted to release large amounts of seed immediately after a fire. The seedlings have a great opportunity to get started in the ash-bed, without competition from other plants. This strategy is usually used by eucalypts which are more susceptible to fire damage as adults.

Eucalypts are now the most widely planted tree in the world. With shortages in timber for paper production, sawlogs, domestic fires and construction the merits of eucalypts for a wide range of uses and sites are now recognised. One of the many hundreds of eucalypt species can usually be found to match special overseas requirements. A limiting factor is that eucalypts will not grow in places where the soil freezes. This essentially limits the Northern Hemisphere cultivated range at about 45 degrees of latitude and this excludes places such as northern Europe, Canada and northern China.

Continued on page 41 . . .

The Gippsland waratah (Telopea oreades) is the only type of waratah to grow into a tree.◄

The most majestic of all Australia's wildflowers, the waratah is a striking plant when in flower. These shrubs and trees have tough, dark green leaves, often toothed, and the individual flowers grow on a dense head.

The waratah (Telopea speciosissima) is the floral emblem of New South Wales. This plant grows to a height of 3 metres or more and can bear over fifty brilliant crimson flower-heads.▼

...rt's desert pea (Clianthus formosus) is found throughout the ...er areas of the continent.

...ought is the typical mood of the arid scrublands but within a ...nth of the violent heavy thunderstorms the wildflowers burst ...o life and the ground is a blaze of colour. (Page 9.)

...e spectacular translucent red flowers of the Sturt desert pea are ...their most striking when seen en masse.

Grevilleas—spider flowers—are among Australia's most attractive group of plants. Colourful and rich in nectar, the flowers have an irresistible attraction to birds. Grevillea confertifolia *(below) and (left)* Grevillea *'Poorinda Peter'*

Hakea francisiana. *Hakeas vary from small shrubs to small trees with a wide range of leaf shapes.* ▲

The fragile Cooktown orchid (Dendrobium bigibbum), *one of the many beautiful wild orchids found in Australia.*◄

The floral emblem of Western Australia, the unusual red and green kangaroo-paw (Anigozanthos manglesii) produces hairy tubular flowers at the end of a long, stiff stem.

'Dwarf Delight', a small variety of kangaroo-paw. Found only i Western Australia, there are eight kinds of kangaroo-paw, whic. resemble the Japanese iris in their growth. ▼

Many Australian wildflowers have adapted to use birds rather than insects as pollinators. The large tubular flowers of the Christmas bell are shaped to ensure that the bird thrusts its head deep into the flower so pollen is deposited on its head.

e colourful bottlebrush is possibly the best known and most
dely cultivated of Australian shrubs.

ttlebrush flowers—crimson, yellow or greenish-white—are
ssed in dense cylindrical spikes and are carried like candles on
tips of the branches. ▼

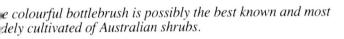

ottlebrush make a brilliant floral display. These hardy, bushy
ants vary in size from 2 metre shrubs to small trees.

A study of perfection—the creamy yellow Banksia oblogifolia. *The banksia was named by the botanist Sir Joseph Banks who discovered it when he came to Australia with Captain James Cook.*

...e of the most attractive of all banksias is the heath-leafed ...riety, Banksia ericifolia.

...anksia integrifolia, a coastal shrub that colours the seascapes of ...ueensland, New South Wales and Victoria.

Wattles are found all over Australia and rank so highly in the affection of the people that they have become the country's floral emblem. There are more than 500 varieties and the flowers range in colour from bright yellow through to deep orange. ▲

Massed pink flowers of the thryptomene, a member of the myrtle family, and the fluffy golden blooms of the acacia colour this outback scene. ▶

Boxleaf wattle (Acacia buxifolia), a bushy yellow-flowered shrub growing in New South Wales. ◀

Few countries have such wealth of wildflowers as Australia. Parts of the continent are carpeted at various seasons with wildflowers of deep purple, vivid red, blue and green—orchids, boronias, pitcher plants, kangaroo-paws and countless species of everlasting flowers. ▲

Late afternoon hues of mauve and gold accentuate the graceful shape of these gum trees at Wyndham, Western Australia. ►

Waterlilies in Kakadu National Park, Northern Territory. ▼

Mosses and ferns clothe the lower levels of temperate rainforest along the shores of Lake St Clair, Tasmania.

Spinifex grass, often called porcupine grass, is found on coastal sand-dunes and inland in warm areas with low rainfall. Spinifex clumps are the home of many geckos, skinks and insects. (Previous page.)

The solitary Cazneaux tree (known as this because it was made famous by Harold Cazneaux's photographs) stands sentinel on a grassy plain in the eastern part of the Flinders Ranges. Gum trees are a symbol of Australia's bushland and pastoral landscapes. ➤

The Australian baobab—the most grotesque tree in the continent. Sometimes called the bottle tree, its name is derived from the bizarre swelling of the trunk caused by internal storage of food and water against long periods of drought. (Left and previous page.)

From Australia's far north to the southernmost part of Tasmania, and from east to west, gum trees are present—wherever trees grow. ►

'Blackboys', or grass-trees, stand out like sentinels on the landscape. These thick-stemmed trees have a crown of long rigid leaves which grow in a dense tuft from which emerges a flower stem 2 metres long.

*The gnarled trunk of a giant fig tree near Wingham in New So
Wales.*

*A river meanders through luxuriant rainforest vegetation. Denrainforest, ranging from tropical to temperate, is found in patalong the northern and eastern coasts of the continent and in
Tasmania.* ➤

Bangalow palms (Archontophoenix cunninghamiana) *adorn ribanks in rainforest areas.*

The silvery, straight, smooth trunks of mature karri forest rise like columns from the undergrowth. The massive karri can grow to more than 60 metres.

North Queensland rainforest. Tree ferns, lush growth and dappled light filtering through the dense canopy are typical of rainforest in the tropical north. (Previous page.)

Scattered gums, boulders and rocky ridges make up the stark landscape on the Edgar Range in the Kimberleys, Western Australia. ▼

Snow gums are an excellent example of the adaptability of eucalypts. They survive above the snow-line, almost overwhelmed by metres of snow during the winter, appearing in fresh spring verdure when the first thaw comes. ▲

Small eucalypts, dazzlingly white barked, are scattered through the rocky spinifex country and are commonly known as 'ghost gums'. (Page 40.)

The hardy mangrove, Fraser Island, Queensland. These trees have adapted to live in tidal shallows where waterlogging and high salt concentrations would kill other trees. (Following page.)

Gum trees typify the Australian landscape. There are more than 500 species of this hardy evergreen which has adapted to all climatic conditions. ►

In parts of Australia large numbers of eucalypts are dying. This is usually given the name 'dieback' and is not a single disease condition but refers to a wide range of problems. One cause of large-scale death of trees is root fungus. The fungus becomes established in an area of forest and, when the soil is wet and warm, can spread quickly. Large areas of jarrah forest in Western Australia and thousands of hectares of silver-topped ash in Victoria are affected. The root fungus lives in the soil and is spread by construction and forestry equipment.

A different problem causes the death of eucalypts in farmlands. Although it too is called 'dieback' it is caused by a range of factors, not just one. One area particularly devastated in recent decades is the northern tablelands of New South Wales based around Armidale although trees in many farming areas face the same threats.

Agricultural practices change the nature of the soil. The watertable may drop, fertility changes with the addition of fertilisers, and the structure of the soil changes with the coming of hard-hooved domestic animals like sheep and cattle. In many areas, most trees were removed by ringbarking at the turn of this century. This practice often left only older shade trees. The dieback that is now occurring is caused by a suite of factors. The over-mature trees are dying and the domestic stock are stopping the growth of new trees. Some trees are dying through the combined effects of lowered watertable and drought. Others succumb to the pressures of leaf-eating insects which are now concentrated on fewer trees. In many parts of rural Australia the appearance of landscape is changing, probably permanently, as a consequence of agricultural practices of the last century.

Acacias

Acacias, or wattles as we know them in Australia, occur throughout the world. However, Australia has over 700 species, which is more than half the known species, and so they are often identified with Australian landscapes. The Australian bush, except for the true rainforests and the most arid deserts, is dominated by the acacias or eucalypts and sometimes both.

Overseas, the flowers of acacias are known as mimosa. However, from the very earliest days in the Australian colonies these showy plants were called 'wattles'. It is commonly believed that this came from the technique for constructing rough huts consisting of cutting bundles of sticks and sealing them into the walls with mud. The plants commonly used for this purpose were the acacias. On the other hand, some early settlers report that some Aborginal tribes called the acacia 'wattah'. Was this a true Aboriginal name and did the name wattle derive from this, or had the Aboriginal tribes already adopted a European name?

All acacia flowers are yellow or pale cream. The differences between the species centre on the leaves, the arrangement of flowers and the form of the plant.

Some acacias have leaves like ferns. One of the first Australian plants ever described was an acacia of this type which was collected by a Dutchman on the Swan River in 1697. The Dutch botanist Burman, lacking the flowers and having just a sample of the leaves, described this acacia as a fern! Most acacias have large, flat 'leaves' which are in fact not leaves at all but highly modified leafstalks. This is hard to believe until you find an occasional 'leaf' with a proper ferny leaf growing from its top. This is a most strange sight. In some acacias even these false leaves are absent or reduced to sharp spines. The flowers on acacias are usually scattered along a branch among the leaves or bundled in large showy clusters at the ends of the branches like the famous Mudgee or golden wattles.

The acacias have a variety of shapes. Some are low ground-hugging shrubs a few centimetres high and many are lofty rainforest trees, such as the Tasmanian blackwood, a fine timber species.

One of the most spectacular of all the acacias is the Cootamundra wattle. Found naturally only around the country town of southern New South Wales with which it shares its name, the Cootamundra wattle has rather sombre blue-grey leaves. However, come August, the brilliant show of yellow flowers covers the tree. It is now widely grown in gardens throughout southern Australia. Unfortunately this tree is relatively short-lived, about fifteen years, and because of this, all acacias now have the same undeserved reputation.

Banksias

Banksias are an exclusively Australian plant. They have large showy flowers which are particularly attractive to pollen-feeding birds and small mammals. About fifty different species are known and the greatest concentration is in the south-western corner of Western Australia.

Banksias were named in honour of the famous English botanist and patron Sir Joseph Banks. History has bestowed the honour of 'father of Australian botany' on this man who accompanied Cook on his 1770 voyage of discovery to Australia's eastern coast.

Banks was fortunate to be born into the great age of the 'Gentlemen amateur'. He was independently wealthy and had a passion for botany and studied at Harrow, Eton and Oxford. At the age of twenty-five he was able to use his social connections and financial resources to have himself, and eight others, given permission to join Cook's expedition to the South Seas. The *Endeavour* set sail on 25 August 1768 and did not return for almost three years. During that time Banks and his colleague Daniel Solander collected 3000 botanical specimens including 1300 new species. All these specimens are now held by the Natural History Museum in London. When the famous Swedish naturalist Linnaeus formally described some of the plants in Banks' collection he named the banksias in his honour.

For four months in 1770 Banks, Solander and their staff collected and drew hundreds of plant specimens along the Australian east coast. Cook named Botany Bay because of

the great quantity of plants Mr Banks and Mr Solander found in this place!

It is a little ironic that the paper that Banks used to dry the plant specimens at Botany Bay were taken from volumes of Milton's *Paradise Lost*. This wealth of plants has now, years later, certainly disappeared under suburban Sydney.

Banksias belong to the large protea family. The family is centred on southern Africa and Australia and probably prompted Charles Darwin's comments relating the plant life of the two areas. The protea family includes such well-known plants as the grevilleas and waratahs.

The banksias are usually shrubs or bushes but some are ground-hugging creepers and one, the Western Australian river banksia, grows into a tree 15 metres high. A feature of this group of plants is the gnarled, twisted appearance of the trunks and branches of mature specimens. The flower spikes have a striking appearance. Growing directly from a branch the flower bloom is usually shaped like a cylinder with large numbers of individual flowers tightly packed together. After the flower dies the woody cone remains. The cones are often used for decorative purposes and have given rise to the 'banksia men' of Australian children's storybooks.

Banksias have developed a number of strategies for surviving the fires which regularly sweep through the coastal forests and heathlands. In some species such as the heath-leafed banksia the entire plant is killed by the fire and a large amount of seed is produced from the many seed-bearing cones which open on the dead plant. The seed is released onto the fire ash-bed and, without competition from other plants, becomes established quickly. In these species it is critical that the next fire does not come until the new plants are old enough to have produced some seed. This may be many years. The fern-leafed banksia survives fire by a combination of seed spread after the fire and by sending shoots from the surviving underground stems. The final strategy for surviving fire is demonstrated by the wallum banksia which has very thick bark. The centre of the trunk is not killed by the fire and new shoots appear on the trunk and branches.

Native orchids

The native orchids can be divided into two obvious groups. The first are the epiphytes, which are those that grow on trees or rocks. The second group are the terrestrial orchids, which grow only in the ground. The Australian epiphytic orchids are found only on the eastern coast in the wetter eucalypt forests and rainforests. The most spectacular of these orchids is the State flower of Queensland, the Cooktown orchid. By far the largest group of Australian orchids are the generally smaller terrestrial species. They range in size from the tiny mosquito orchids to the large swamp orchids of coastal Queensland which has a flower stalk up to 2 metres high and the largest flower of any Australian orchid.

Curiously, the extraordinary plants of Australia have never seemed to evoke the same incredulity as some of the continent's animals. Two plants which must set the record straight are the underground orchids. These orchids are unlikely to win a flower show with their tiny flowers but are remarkable in that they grow and flower underground! Two species of these subterranean orchids are known: one from a few localities from Brisbane to the Blue Mountains, near Sydney, and the other from south-western Western Australia.

The underground orchids live on a fungus which grows on the roots of certain gum trees and broom-bushes. The flowers are probably pollinated by small ants, termites and beetles which are attracted to its strong smell. Once the seed is produced it is pushed to the surface to be dispersed.

Recent research in southern Australia has revealed a fascinating relationship between Australian native plants and birds. Many bird species are adapted to feed on nectar from flowers and for many years it has been known that birds, particularly honeyeaters, contributed to the pollination of flowers. Pollination is usually done by the plants themselves or by insects. However, it was not realised how significant birds were and how many plants depended on birds as pollinators. In south-western Western Australia over 600 species of plants depend on birds as the primary pollinators of their flowers. These include many of the banksias, kangaroo-paws, bottlebrushes, grevilleas and honeyflowers.

As a consequence, the flowers of these plants are adapted to attract birds not insects. Since birds have no sense of smell other features are needed to attract them. Bird-attracting flowers are predominantly red in colour but yellow and white are also important. The most common flower is bowl-shaped like the eucalypts. Somehow birds are able to detect which plants are producing the most nectar and concentrate their feeding on these. It appears that the plants which are able to attract the greatest number of birds are liable to be the most successful and produce more seed. Many marsupials are now also being recognised as having an important pollinating role and these include the tiny honey possum, feather-tailed glider and pygmy possums.

Floral emblems

Flowers have long been used as symbols. The significance of many plants such as ivy, hawthorn and palms goes back to the folklore and religious beliefs of the European ancestors of most Australians.

It is only natural that Australians should seek to identify with the native plants of their country and use them as symbols. Native flowers form a natural living heritage with links through botanical history to the first European exploration of the continent.

Although the golden wattle enjoys the status of being Australia's national floral emblem it is without any official declaration. This wattle appears as the background for the national Coat of Arms. The designs of the insignia of the Order of Australia are based on an individual ball of wattle flowers. Australian sportsmen and women always wear gold and green which is claimed to be based on the colours of the golden wattle. Thus by default rather than official patronage the golden wattle is Australia's national floral emblem.

Golden wattle grows as a small tree up to 8 metres in height. It is found in open woodlands in South Australia, Victoria, New South Wales and the Australian Capital Territory. It is a resilient plant which reproduces vigorously after fire. This wattle grows well in cultivation and has been widely planted overseas.

The floral emblem for New South Wales is the waratah. The brilliant red flowers appear in the bush near Sydney in spring and early summer. The scientific name is based on Greek words meaning 'beautiful handsome plant seen from afar'. The flowers are really quite magnificent but the shrub is rather disappointing. The rank woody shrub appears not to truly compliment such beautiful blooms. The waratah grows only in the infertile sandstone soils in the immediate vicinity of Sydney.

An interesting story concerning the selection of the national and New South Wales floral emblems throws some light on the rivalry between Australia's two most populous States. Although the arguments could be debated at length, the brilliant red flower of the waratah is probably a stronger and more attractive symbol than the paler, more open wattle bloom. The waratah also belongs to a group of plants which are found only in Australia. Wattles on the other hand grow in many other parts of the world. However, waratahs don't grow in Victoria and the golden wattle grows in both States. This has settled the matter. The conflict has been so great that the official shovels used by the Govenor-General and his party at the launching of Canberra in 1913 were decorated with two floral blooms: the waratah and the golden wattle!

Victoria's floral emblem, the common heath, grows in Victoria, of course, and neighbouring States. The common heath has a range of flower colours, from white to scarlet; however, it was the pink fern that was chosen as the State's flower. The pink-flowered common heath is found only in the Grampian mountains in western Victoria.

Kangaroo-paws are found only in Western Australia. The brilliant red and green Mangles' kangaroo-paw is the floral symbol of the State. Kangaroo-paws are curious, lily-like plants with the flowers resembling outstretched fingers on the end of thin, long arms. The flowers are covered in small hairs giving them a velvet appearance. The flowers of Mangles' kangaroo-paw are collected for the fresh and dried flower market and many plants are exported. Kangaroo-paws are only some of the hundreds of beautiful plant species which make up the world-famous springtime wildflower displays in the bushland around Perth.

The Sturt's desert pea is the emblem for South Australia and unlike the kangaroo-paw has no regular flowering season. Typical of many desert plants, it flowers in response to rain. The brilliant black-centred red flowers make a carpet of colour contrasting brilliantly with the sombre desert hues. After the plant flowers the hard seeds are shed and survive many years before conditions favour germination.

The Northern Territory's floral emblem, Sturt's desert rose, also celebrates one of Australia's most widely travelled inland explorers, Captain Charles Sturt. Sturt made observations of both the desert pea and desert rose, which now bear his name. The desert rose is a small desert shrub with dark green leaves. The flowers which often appear in late winter betray the desert rose's affinity with hibiscuses. The petals are mauve and the flowers have dark red centres.

The desert homes of the South Australian and Northern Territory emblems are a long way from the wet tropical home of Queensland's flower. The Cooktown orchid is, for an Australian orchid, very impressive. Up to twenty large white or mauve flowers are produced on a flower stalk and these make a fine indoor cut-flower display. They grow in the wild attached to tree trunks or exposed rock faces in wet forests of far northern Queensland.

The Cooktown orchid became Queensland's floral emblem as a result of a competition. In 1959 when the State was preparing to celebrate its centenary several plants were suggested as possible emblems. A Brisbane newspaper held a competition and over 10 000 entries were received. The Cooktown orchid was the clear winner with a grevillea as runner-up. It is a reflection of many Australians' perception of their native plants that third place in the competition went to a widely planted Mexican import, the poinsettia. In finally deciding on the floral emblem for the State the government wanted an easily cultivated native Queensland plant, which was decorative and distinctive in appearance as well as being maroon, Queensland's official colour.

The largest plant chosen as a State floral emblem is the Tasmanian blue gum. With a height of 70 metres and a trunk diameter of 2 metres it is hardly a plant to add to a flower bed!

The Tasmanian blue gum is a tree of the tall forests of south-eastern Tasmania and parts of Victoria. It is a valuable timber tree and is used for heavy construction such as poles, sleepers and piles. The tree is widely grown in New Zealand, South Africa, California and the Mediterranean region.

Unfortunately, the flowers are quite inaccessible and the tree is hardly suitable for a home gardener. The blue gum has not become as popular as a symbol as it might and this is probably due in part to its unfamiliarity to the average Tasmanian.

By contrast with the blue gum, the Australian Capital Territory has one of the smallest floral emblems. The delicate royal bluebell is a native of the high-country forests of the Australian Capital Territory, New South Wales and Victoria. The small violet-blue flowers are only 3 centimetres across but emerge in small clusters. This floral emblem is easily cultivated and grows from seed, cuttings or division of the roots. It is suitable for growing in small gardens or pots and this makes it accessible to many would-be gardeners.

Introduced plants

Australia's floral appearance has been altered for all time by the introduction of a wide variety of plant species from all over the world. Since no Australian plants provide any significant foods for Europeans all of the cultivated food plants are introduced. Many of the country's worst weed pests have come from seemingly innocuous exotic garden plants.

The most famous example of this is the prickly pear. It started originally as a curious pot-plant in a garden at Scone in the Hunter Valley in 1839. Within sixty years this aggressive weed had covered more than 4 million hectares of grazing country in southern Queensland. Hundreds of thousands of native birds were killed in an attempt to stop the spread of the seed. By 1925, some 25 million hectares of eastern Australia were covered with the pest and it was spreading at the rate of 100 hectares an hour. Those attempting to control the pest were lucky. An insect predator from the prickly pear's native homeland was introduced and the cactus disappeared almost overnight.

This remarkable result has not been achieved for other weed pests on anything like the same scale since. The best form of control is to keep potential new weed species from becoming established in the first place. Australia has very strict quarantine controls to protect the country's agricultural industries as well as the unique animals and plants.

Index

Numbers in *italics* denote colour photographs.

Acknowledgements

Douglass Baglin: pages 18 above, 35, 37.
John Baker: pages 17 below, 24, 30 below, 36.
Robert Berthold: page 17 above.
John Carnemolla: pages 9, 11 below, 25, 30 above, 31, 34 below.
Ron Dorman: page 15 below.
Leigh Hemmings: pages 38–9.
Owen Hughes: pages 21, 26–7, 34 above.
Noeline Kelly: pages 15 above left, 29.
S. W. Lowry: page 20 below.
Greg Miller: page 13 right.
Robert Nelson: page 18 below.
Outback Photography: page 11 above.
Fritz Prenzel: pages 10 above left, 10 below, 12, 13 left, 14, 15 above right, 16, 32–3.
Profile Photography: page 28.
Derek Roff: pages 19, 20 above, 22–3.
Joseph Spiteri: page 10 above right.